Hi everybody! Welcome to the sneak preview of our next Book!!!

its ALL About a character we invented way back in Kindergarten!

Its a collection of **rare mini** comics...

Tongue of Justise

DOG Man 2

... and more than 100 pages of never before seen stuff!

ALL NEW

So WAG Your Tails and HowL at The MOON...

DOG MAN

The Adventures of DOG MAN is **COMING** SOON!!!

The following **PREVIEW** has been approved for **KIDS ONLY** by Tree House Comics, INC.

The Graphic Novel Advertised has been rated

| KO | KIDS ONLY |

No Boring old grown ups, ok?

You've **Laffed** with Super Diaper Baby...

Tee Hee!!!

... and **THRILLED** with Ook and Gluk...

So Long, Sucka!

Now, get ready for the **NEWEST** crime fighting sensation from the awesome folks at Tree House Comix.

that's us!!!

Me too!

In a world where evil cats wreak havoc on the innocent...

Haw Haw Haw!

... and sinister angelfish poison the souls of the meek......

fooey!

If You Read onLy **ONE BOOK** Next Year, weLL... You really Should Try to read more than that. We're Just sayin'.....

But Don't Forget to Read this one, too!

TREE HOUSE COMIX

DOG MAN
The World's Greatest cop

ACTION 'N' LAFFS!

IN FULL COLoR!

Flip-o-RAMA in every ChapTer!

BY **DAV PiLKeY**

Featuring **TRiPLE FLi P-O-RAMA**

Left Hand here

You'LL HowL with Laughter.

You'LL scratch with Suspense!

You'LL Scoot on the carpet with JOY!

Right THuMB here

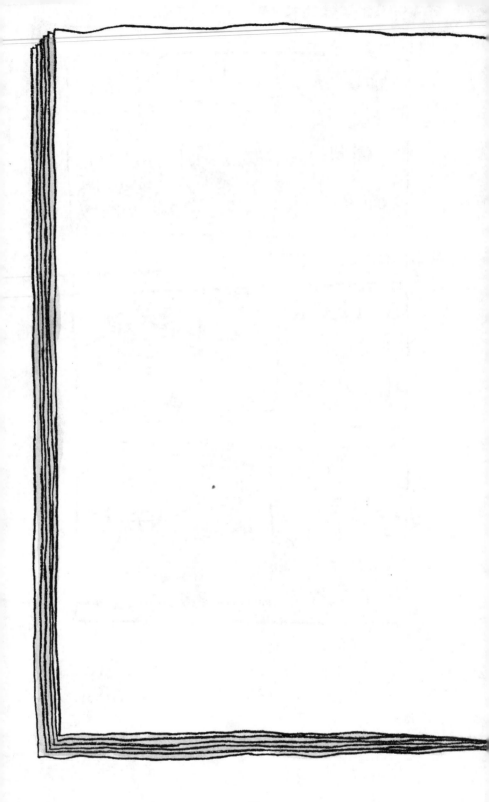

You'll Howl with Laughter.	
You'll Scratch with Suspense!	
You'll Scoot on the Carpet with Joy!	

Bathtime
for
Dog man

RIGHT
THUMB
Here

Bathtime
For
Dog man

this Has BeeN a presenta- tion oF tree House Comix INc. ALL RiGhts Reserved

SPLAP!

DOG MAN!!!

Later

Why You Gotta Bust my chops, huh?

You Better straighten up or else!!

Dog man Promised to Be a better man...

...But could he be a better Dog?

Petey Sneaked to the police station...

and put a air Freshener in every cop car.

Haw Haw!!!

soon every cop will be my slave!!!

LATER

RING

HELLO?

theres a Bank robbery

where?

at the Bank!

Oh.

..Except one!

DOG MAN LiKed to drive with his head OUT the window.

So he never Smelled the eviL air Freshener!

Dog man arrived at The Bank...

... JUST aS PETeY was escaping.

up the stairs they ran.

DOG man was getting super thirsty...

Then he saw it!!!

glistening... sparkling... Refreshing...

COOL as a mountain Stream...

Thirst Quenching and DeliciOUS...

DOGMAN had to act fast! So He thought up a 3-step plan.

Step 1

Retrieve the
Antidote

RiGhT
THuMB
HeRe

Step 1

Retrieve the Antidote

the anti-
dote was
on the
FLOor...

BUT HOW COULD
He use it???

FLIP·O·
RAMA

Left
Hand Here

step 2

Collect the antidote

49

RIGHT
THUMB
HeRe

step 2

Collect the antidote

The antidote was on DOG man's tongue.

now came the ~~fun~~ Fun Part!!!

TRIPLE FLIP-O-RAMAS

animate the action cheesily. Heres How:

Hold Book Open Like this...

Flip Page Back and Forth.

add Your own sound effects!

Left Hand Here

RIGHT
THUMB
HERE

step 3

apply
the
antidote

! ! !

HOW 2 DRAW

Hey, Kids, Be the first in your class to master the art of Drawing Dog Man and Petey!!!

It's ~~real~~ easy! Just grab a pencil and we'll show you HOW!!!

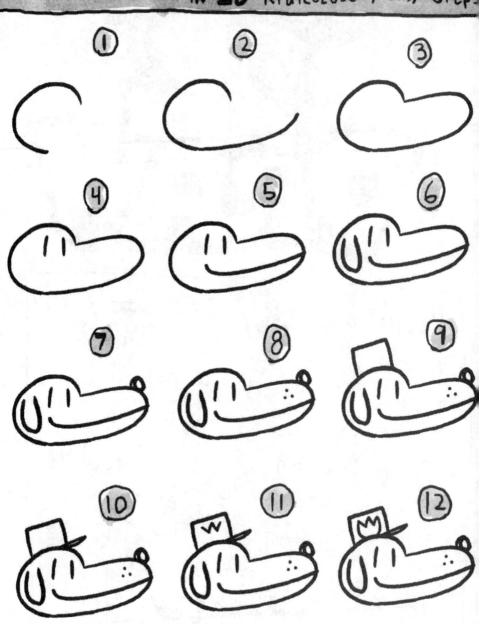

BE EXPRESSive!!!

Happy   Happier   Supa Happy

Worried   Sad   Determined

ascared   Angry   sleepy

HOW 2 DRAW PETEY

in 24 Ridiculously easy steps.

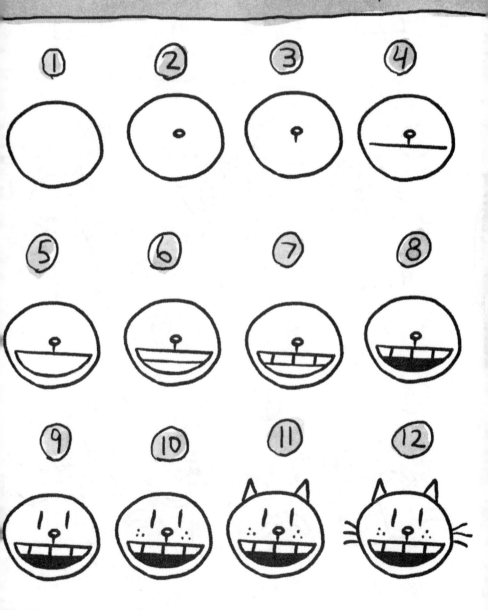

BE EXPRESSIVE

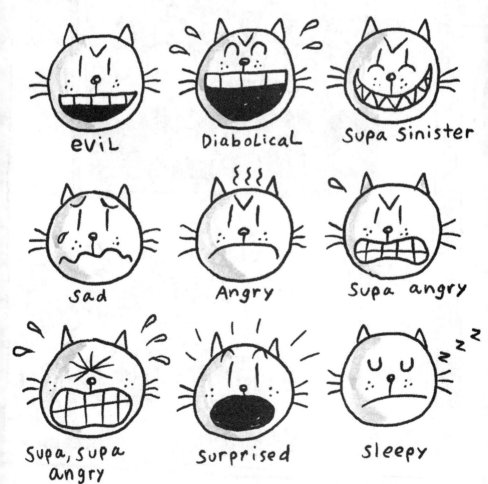

evil

Diabolical

Supa Sinister

Sad

Angry

Supa angry

Supa, Supa angry

Surprised

sleepy

TREE HOUSE COMIX

DOG MAN
The World's Greatest Cop

ACTION 'N' LAFFS!

IN FULL COLOR!

FLIP-O-RAMA in every Chapter!

BY DAV PILKEY

"It's the greatest Book about a Dog-headed Cop Ever Written!"
— George's Grandma

"Dog-Gone Funny!"
— Harold's Grampa

"I hated every Page!"
— MR. KRUPP

BEG FOR iT!

Whine For iT!

Fetch Your Copy ON AUGUST 30, 2016!